This Book Belongs To: _____

Dear Fellow Friend of Jumpstart,

Remember when you were a child and reading was like stepping into an adventure written just for you?

When we read with children, every story is an exciting and fun learning opportunity that feeds their minds and opens up the world around them. Key research indicates that the number of books in a child's home is a major predictor of future reading ability, and reading with a young child sets the cornerstone for future success.

For the past three years, Jumpstart's Read for the Record Campaign has provided more than 500,000 books to children and families who need them most and raised critical awareness of the importance of reading. Jumpstart also works intensively with children throughout the year to develop the literacy, language and social skills that are vital to their school success. In fact, this year alone Jumpstart will provide children with more than one million hours of language and literacy programming.

Read this book with us on October 8, 2009, and together we can make a difference in the lives of children everywhere.

On behalf of Jumpstart and children and families across America, thank you for supporting Jumpstart.

Matt Lauer   Meredith Vieira

Dear Reader,

LL Cool J is a talented entertainer, actor, author, recording artist, two-time Grammy Award winner, and NAACP Image Award winner.

I am thrilled to once again be involved in Jumpstart's Read for the Record to support Jumpstart's year-round early literacy efforts with children in low-income communities.

We all need a jump start in our lives. My grandparents and mother were my early jump start. When I was young, they read to me, sparking my imagination. That early love of words and stories is the cornerstone of my career. I can't imagine being where I am now without their support or without books in my life.

I am involved with Jumpstart because they work directly with thousands of children across our country to help them succeed in school and in life. You can be a part of what Jumpstart does by reading with me on October 8. Register to read and support Jumpstart at **www.readfortherecord.org**.

Together we can make this year's campaign even bigger and ensure that all our children receive the "jump start" they need to thrive.

Reading is cool.

Best wishes,

Dear Friend of Jumpstart,

I've been in love with books as long as I can remember. As a child they were my best friends; as an adult, reading continues to enrich me, especially working in the theatre.

More importantly, as a parent, I believe it is my responsibility to pass on this love of reading to my children. I read to my children within hours of the first time I held them.

Jumpstart shares my passion and understands how critical literacy skills are to our children's success in kindergarten and beyond. I'm proud to support Jumpstart and Jumpstart's Read for the Record and ask you to join me.

Register to read *The Very Hungry Caterpillar* with me on October 8 at **www.readfortherecord.org** as we set a world record for children.

Keep reading!

Mary-Louise Parker, a Tony-, Emmy- and Golden Globe–winning actress, reads with record breaking participant.

Thank you for supporting Jumpstart
by purchasing this book!

A Growing Movement

Jumpstart's Read for the Record is getting bigger every year. Let's make 2009 the best year yet!

Since 2006:
- 1 million children have been a part of Jumpstart's Read for the Record
- 500,000 campaign books have been donated to children in need

The proceeds from this limited edition copy of *The Very Hungry Caterpillar* support Jumpstart, a national children's literacy organization.

Jumpstart's mission is to ensure that all children in America enter school prepared to succeed. Year-round, Jumpstart recruits and trains thousands of people to work one-to-one with children in low-income communities, helping preschoolers develop the language, literacy and social skills they need in school and in life.

Presented in partnership with Pearson, Read for the Record is your chance to experience for yourself the importance of Jumpstart's work every day in preschools across the United States. Please join us on October 8, 2009, as together we read *The Very Hungry Caterpillar* in a record-breaking celebration of reading, service, and fun—all in support of America's preschoolers. In the process, we aim to set a new world record for the greatest number of people reading the same book on the same day. (It's a record we've improved upon every year since Jumpstart's Read for the Record began!)

Participating is easy.

If you're reading this, you're already holding the official book of Jumpstart's Read for the Record 2009 Campaign.

Here's what to do next:
- Be counted. Register to read today at **www.readfortherecord.org**. You'll find everything you need to be ready to have your participation counted on October 8.
- Get others involved. Spread the word and consider helping others read with us by donating a limited edition campaign book to a child in need. Visit **www.readfortherecord.org** to find out how.

Thank you for reading for the record!

Make the Most of Reading Together

When reading with a child in your life, remember these simple ways to share the joy of reading:

- Set aside time to read every day. Create a special time and place for reading.
- Make reading fun and interactive. Be playful and never forget to enjoy the story!
- Have a conversation. Explain new words, make comments, and ask questions.
- Read the book again! Your child learns more each time you reread the story.

Build Language and Knowledge Through Reading

Stories hold endless potential to develop a child's imagination and help build a greater understanding of the world. Introducing a book for the first time is an exciting, almost magical experience. *The Very Hungry Caterpillar* has a very busy week and whimsical eating adventures. The first time through, enjoy discovering the story events and characters. Here are some things you can talk about as you read together:

Take time to provide a simple explanation for words that might be new to your child.

- **tiny**—very, very small
- **caterpillar**—looks like a hairy worm with lots of legs
- **stomachache**—when your tummy hurts
- **nibble**—to take very little bites of something
- **cocoon**—a small house the caterpillar makes to sleep and grow in

Talk about what happens to the tiny caterpillar.

- Point out how tiny the caterpillar is when he pops out of the egg.
- Spend time examining the cocoon. "What do you think the caterpillar is doing in the cocoon?"
- When the butterfly emerges from the cocoon, ask questions like, "Were you surprised when the butterfly came out of the cocoon?"
- Talk about the journey of the caterpillar. "How do you think the caterpillar changed in the story?"
- Relate the story to the child's life. "How are you like the caterpillar? When do you feel like a butterfly?"

When you return to the story there are many opportunities to talk about math and science concepts such as counting, sequencing, and size, and how a caterpillar becomes a butterfly. You'll also notice a connection to days of the week and the importance of a balanced diet. Explore these themes and concepts following your child's interests.

Read It Again!

The Very Hungry Caterpillar will fast become a favorite story for your child, who will want to read it again and again. Each time your child will absorb more from the story and can take on a larger role retelling it to you!

As you reread the book, engage your child in retelling the story. Tell your child that now it is his or her turn to tell the story. Just read pages that will help your child remember parts of the story. Pause on pages and use a question or two to guide your child in making connections to the story and content as well as to his or her experiences. Here are some other ideas to try:

Ask your child questions to uncover motivation. "Why do you think the caterpillar was so hungry? Why do you think the caterpillar ate the green leaf?"

Talk about quantities and compare colors of the various fruits and other food. "How many plums are on this page? Which are the red fruits?"

Encourage your child to make predictions. "What do you think will happen next?"

Pause when the caterpillar changes and ask questions to help your child draw connections to his or her own experiences:

- "Why do you think the caterpillar has a stomachache?"
- "Have you ever had a stomachache?"
- "What made your stomach hurt?"
- "How did you feel when you had a stomachache?"

Invite your child to make observations: "What are the similarities between the butterfly and the caterpillar? How are they different?"

Ask the child to think about his or her own life. "What do you do to get bigger and bigger? How do you change as you get bigger? How are you like the butterfly?"

Beyond the Story

Let's discover! Children love to retell stories and connect them to their own lives. Here are some fun and easy things you can do to connect the story of *The Very Hungry Caterpillar* to your child's life.

Re-create the story.

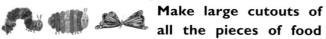 **Make large cutouts of all the pieces of food in the story.** Gather some old socks and provide things like buttons, sequins, fabric markers, and construction paper to use as decorations, turning a sock into a caterpillar. Invite your child to retell the story using the sock caterpillar and the food. Hint: Make the holes in the food large enough for your child to put the caterpillar through!

Make a felt story board. Take a piece of cardboard and cover it with some felt. Cut out different pieces of felt to make a caterpillar and food items from the book. Children can then use this story board to retell the story. Put everything in a bag and you have a great car activity.

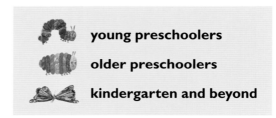

young preschoolers

older preschoolers

kindergarten and beyond

 **Make a play.** This is a very fun activity for a few children to do together—big brothers and sisters will love it, too!

Go on a nature walk.

Explore the natural world around you and see if you and your child can find eggs, caterpillars, or butterflies. Talk about what you find—or don't find.

Take a trip to the grocery store.

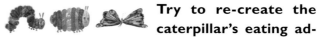 **Try to re-create the caterpillar's eating adventure.** Perhaps your child would like to try some of the fruits and foods that the caterpillar ate. Make a grocery list together. Include pictures and written words. Encourage your child to write and draw.

What do you eat every day?

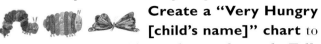Create a "Very Hungry [child's name]" chart to track what your child eats during the week. Talk about the various foods and record them on the chart. You can talk about the days of the week and all the different things your child ate to produce a healthful, balanced diet.

Visit your local science center or butterfly house.

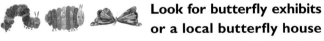Look for butterfly exhibits or a local butterfly house where you and your child can go and watch butterflies.

Older children might enjoy a trip to a museum of natural sciences to learn more about the life cycles of butterflies or other creatures.

Make your own book or story.

Ask your child to pick his or her own insect. Then have your child create a journey for the insect including an obstacle and how the insect overcomes it. Allow the insect to have its victorious "butterfly" moment. Then find some paper and let your child draw the story, cut out pictures from old magazines, or use ripped or cut colored paper, just as Eric Carle did. Offer to write your child's words below the pictures.

Older children might like to use a digital camera to take pictures and make their own story.

Add these books to your home library and enjoy them again and again!

We would like to extend special thanks to Laura Berk, Susan Neuman, Judith Schickedanz, and Ruth Strubank for their guidance and contributions to this content.

THE VERY HUNGRY CATERPILLAR

by Eric Carle

PHILOMEL BOOKS

ALSO BY ERIC CARLE

The Very Busy Spider
The Very Quiet Cricket
The Very Lonely Firefly
The Very Clumsy Click Beetle
1, 2, 3 to the Zoo
Animals Animals
Dragons Dragons
Draw Me a Star
Dream Snow
The Honeybee and the Robber
Little Cloud
Mister Seahorse
"Slowly, Slowly, Slowly," Said the Sloth
Today Is Monday

This special edition published in 2009 by Philomel Books,
a division of Penguin Young Readers Group.
Photo on page v © 2008 by Gary Gershoff.
Photos on page iii © 2008 by Djamilla Rosa Cochran.
Photo on page viii © 2008 by Michael Warren. All rights reserved.

Library of Congress catalog card number: 79-13202
This edition ISBN 978-0-399-25437-6

For my sister Christa

In the light of the moon
a little egg lay on a leaf.

One Sunday morning the warm sun came up and—pop!—out of the egg came a tiny and very hungry caterpillar.

He started to look for some food.

On Tuesday
he ate through
two pears,
but he was
still hungry.

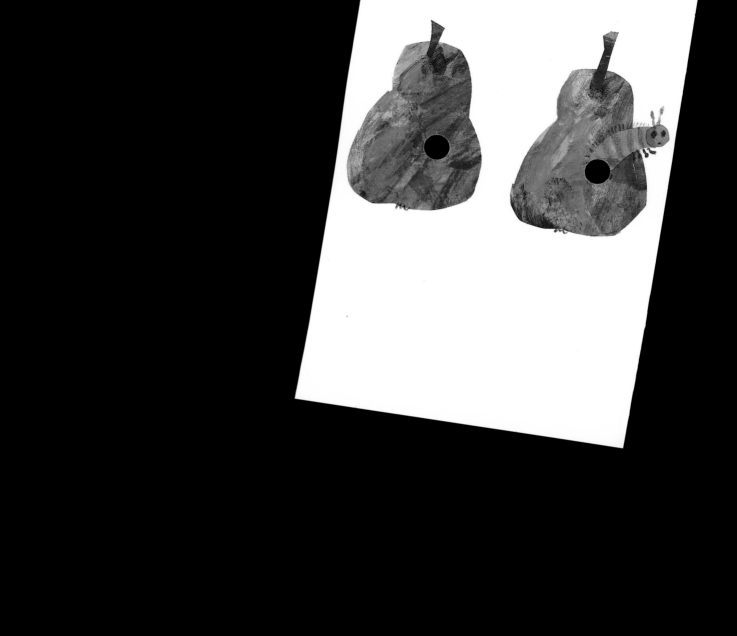

On Wednesday
he ate through
three plums,
but he was still
hungry.

On Thursday
he ate through
four strawberries,
but he was still
hungry.

On Friday
he ate through
five oranges,
but he was still
hungry.

On Saturday
he ate through
one piece of
chocolate cake, one ice-cream cone, one pickle, one slice of Swiss cheese, one slice of salami,

ne lollipop, one piece of cherry pie, one sausage, one cupcake, and one slice of watermelon.

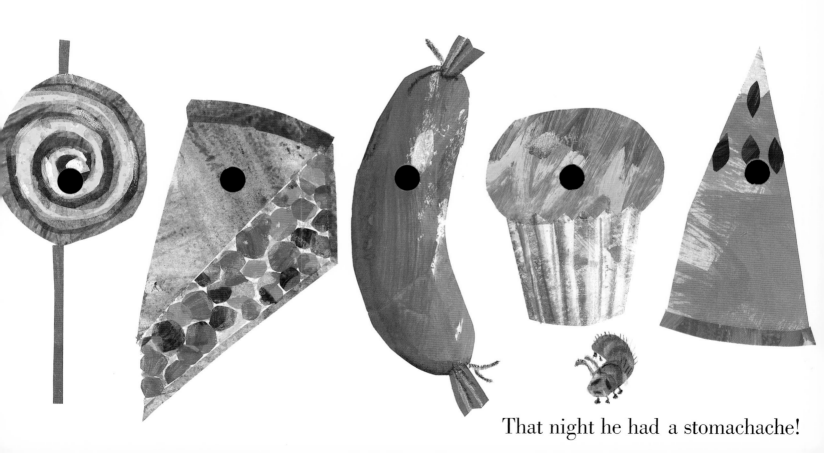

That night he had a stomachache!

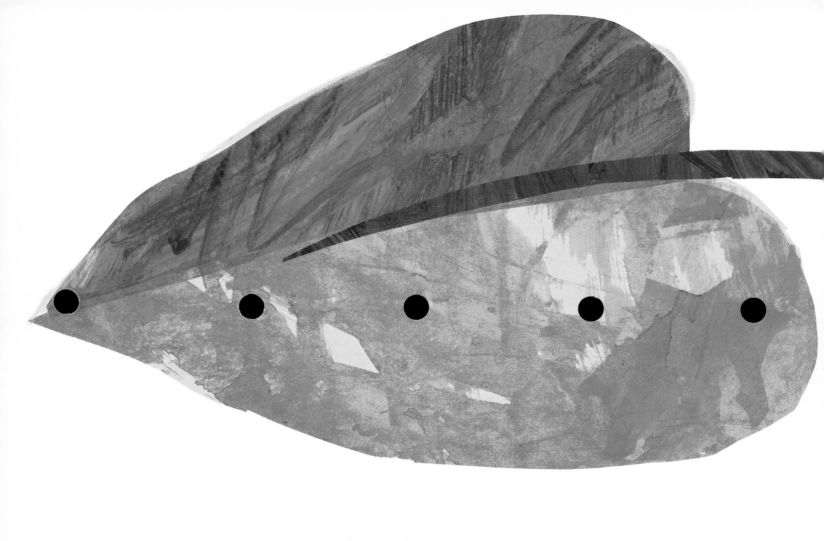

The next day was Sunday again.
The caterpillar ate through
one nice green leaf,
and after that he felt
much better.

Now he wasn't hungry any more—and he wasn't a little caterpillar any more.
He was a big, fat caterpillar.

He built a small house, called a cocoon, around himself. He stayed inside for
more than two weeks. Then he nibbled a hole in the cocoon, pushed his way out and . . .

he was a beautiful butterfly!

About This Book

As we again get ready to break the world record for the largest shared reading event ever, all of us at Jumpstart thank the people and businesses of Pearson for their continuing support.

This custom limited edition of the Philomel Books classic *The Very Hungry Caterpillar* has been published and distributed by Pearson, ensuring that 100 percent of the proceeds from the sale of this book directly supports Jumpstart's work with children from low-income communities across America.

In addition to underwriting the book at the heart of Jumpstart's Read for the Record Campaign, Pearson and its people are again making plans to help set a new world record on October 8. Across the U.S. and around the world, they're also helping teachers, libraries, civic officials, and community organizations to plan reading events and highlight the importance and the power of reading. The Pearson Foundation is also providing more than 200,000 copies of *The Very Hungry Caterpillar* to at-risk children in school districts and community organizations worldwide.

Since 2001, Pearson businesses—Pearson Education, the Financial Times Group, and the Penguin Group—have shared Jumpstart's goal of ensuring that every child in America enters school prepared to succeed. Please find out more about the Pearson-Jumpstart Partnership and about all the ways that Pearson helps people around the world to live and learn by visiting **www.pearsonfoundation.org.**